The Usborne

Pocket

Fashion Drawing Book

Written by **Fiona Watt**

Designed and illustrated by **Antonia Miller**

Additional design by Non Figg and Vicky Barker

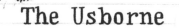

Create outfits for the designer dolls.

2

3

4

Decorate or fill in these bags, then design some of your own.

Draw party clothes, ballgowns, evening dresses or whatever you like.

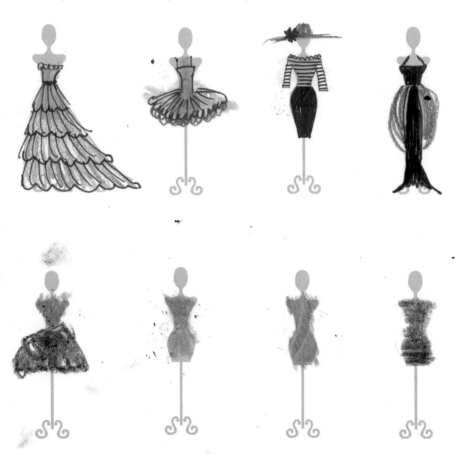

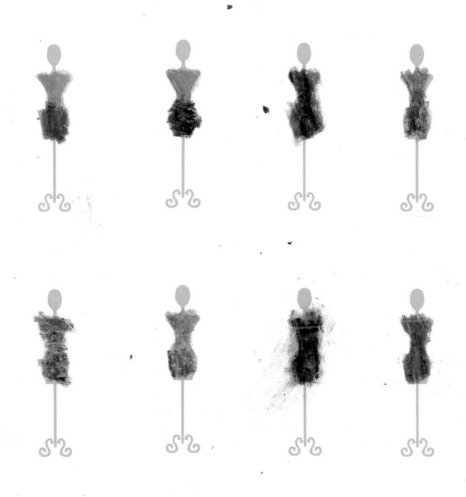

7

Design a Spring fashion collection.

Fill the department store with busy shoppers.

Add clothes on the racks and things on display.

Design some
stylish hats.

Designer tip: draw the hat first, then add the hair.

13

Decorate the
dresses for a
movie premiere.

Fill the pages with clothes, hats and bags.

Jenna has adhd what is that?

You get lost in thought. it's hard to sit still

You get off the subject.

You say things without thinking. it's hard to concentrate.

Copy these patterns or design some of your own.

18

Add lots of hair accessories, earrings and different styles of glasses.

Fill in the
winter coats
with deep or
strong shades.

23

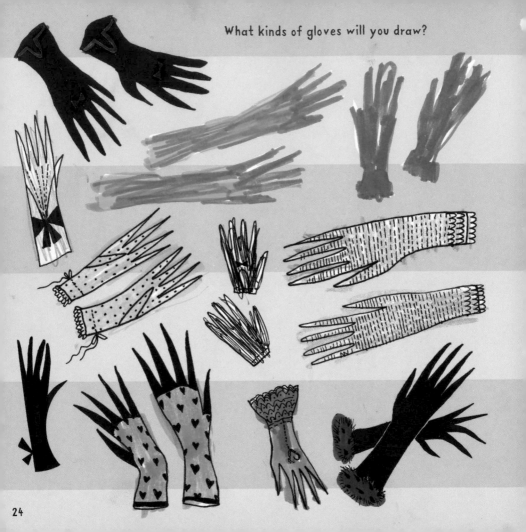

24

25

Create a fashion collection of casual outfits.

Fill in this flowery fabric.

28

Embellish the clothes on these catwalk models.

Decorate these prom dresses with bows, sashes and dazzling diamonds.

34

Shoes... boots...
heels... flats...
Fill the page.

Draw lace or patterns on these ballgowns.

Add more beads and
jewels to the necklaces
and pendants.

Design two elegant hats.

Be a fabric designer by filling the squares with patterns.

42

Design outfits for these models in a catwalk show.

Are they coordinated or are they all different?

Pale or bright shades? You choose...

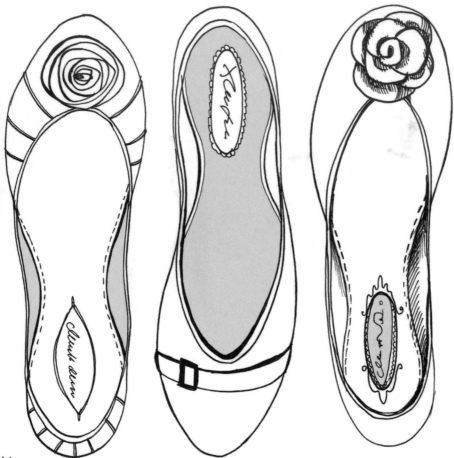

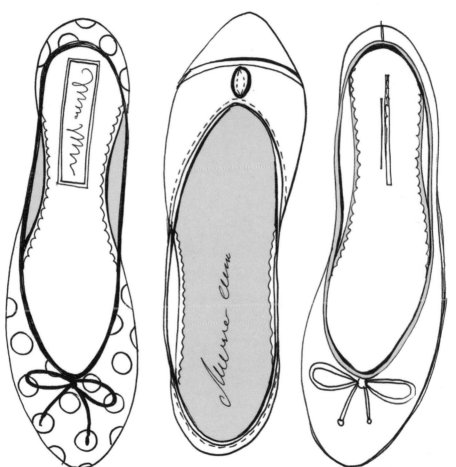

47

Design delicate patterns on these wedding dresses.

49

Fill in this fabric design. Draw more details in the shapes, if you want to.

50

Fill this window display with more bags.

Fill in these
dressmaker's
buttons.

Add dresses, hats and other accessories to these dolls.

Draw exquisite designs on these perfume bottles.

Complete these elegant outfits inspired by the 1920s.

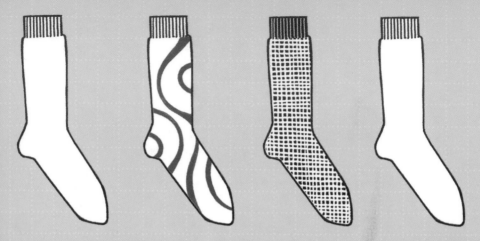

Draw patterns on these socks. Make them bold and bright or pale and simple.

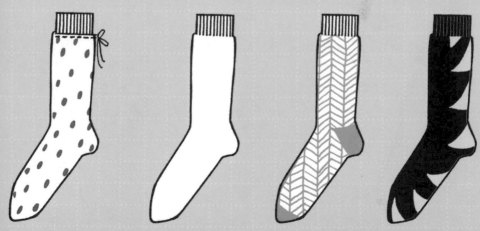

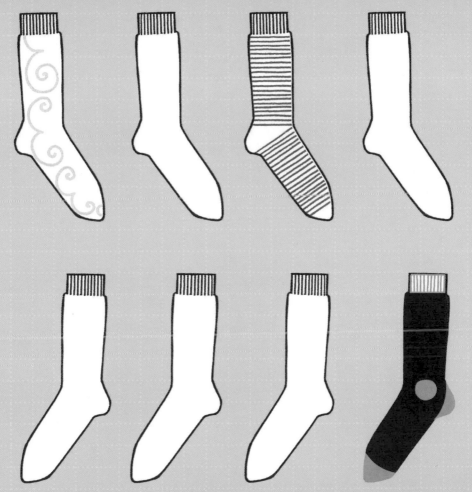

Create lots of different hairstyles.

Add earrings, necklaces and other accessories, too.

Weekend shopping. Fill the street with busy shoppers.

Draw more shoes to fill these pages.

Draw big, bold patterns or delicate designs.

You could draw patterns on the background, too.

Fashion designs
inspired by the 1960s.

72

Fill the dresses with bold, bright patterns.

73

Add windows, doors and roof tiles to the buildings.

Then, fill the streets with late-night shoppers.

Finish this fashion designer's sketchbook.

Ideas for dress fabrics

76

Draw some fabric ideas of your own.

Draw outfits on these shop mannequins.

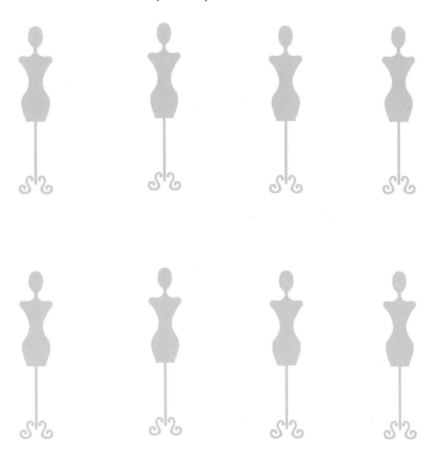

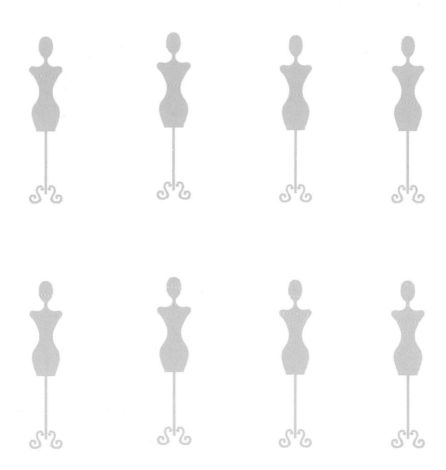

Accessorize...

81

Design a button collection.

Add details to the items in this window display, then fill them in.

Lace patterns to copy, or design some of your own.

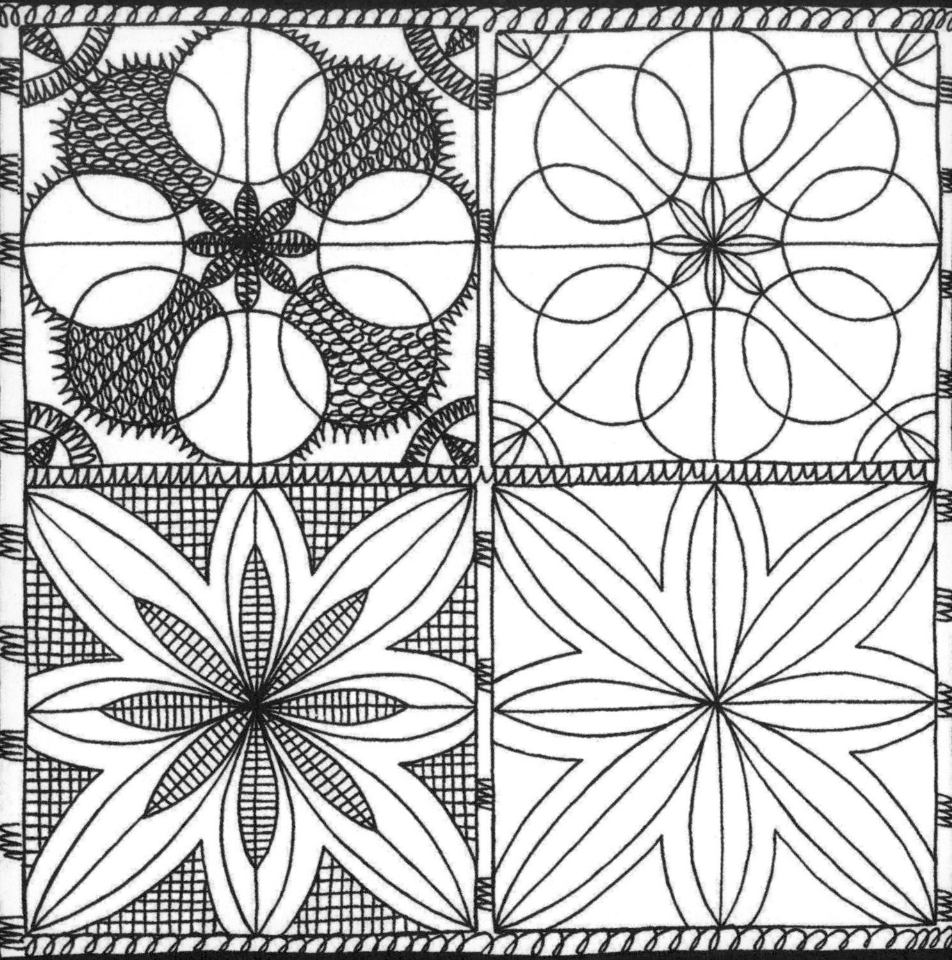

Add hair and make-up.

89

Design outfits for a casual weekend.

Fill in the faces at a catwalk show.

Add more faces in the crowd.

Designer dresses to decorate.

Be a fabric designer and fill each shape with a different pattern.

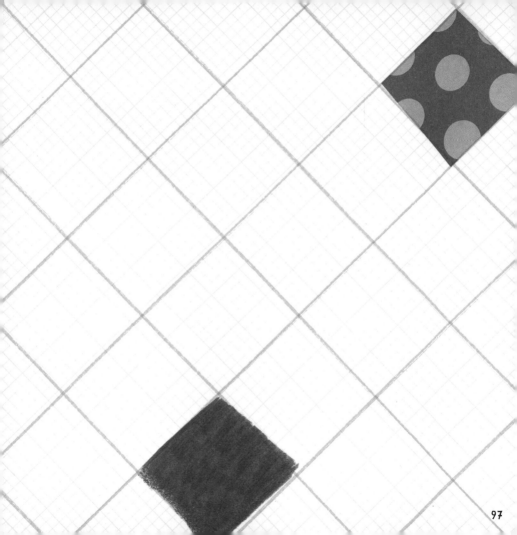

Draw a different outfit on each figure.

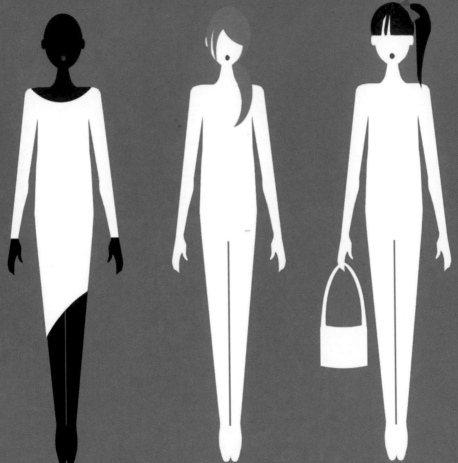

Decorate the nails.

Then, add some rings.

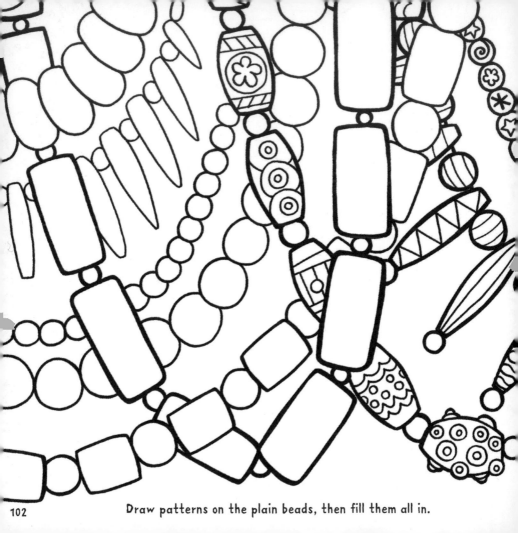

Draw patterns on the plain beads, then fill them all in.

Create some summery designs for these T-shirts.

Draw patterns
on all the
fabric samples.

Be a hair stylist. Draw hair on these two stylish models.

What will each girl choose to wear today?

Copy these lace patterns or use the shapes to design some of your own.

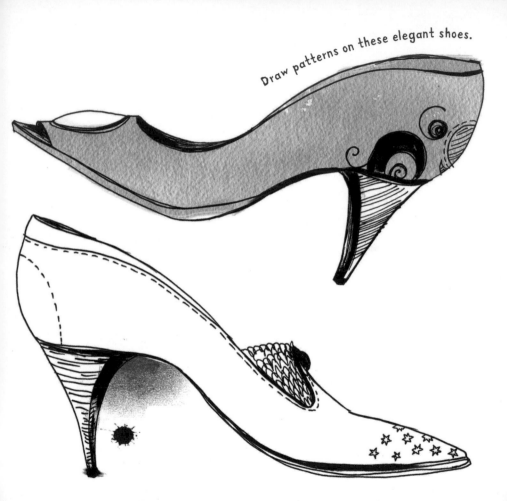

Draw patterns on these elegant shoes.

Try swirls or curls, stars, spots and dots.

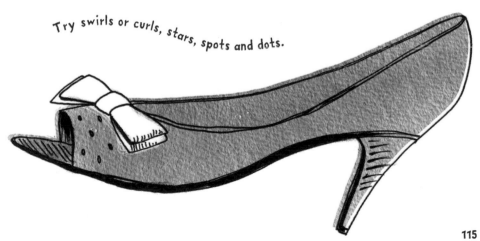

Fill the pages with lots more accessories.

Design a Summer festival collection.

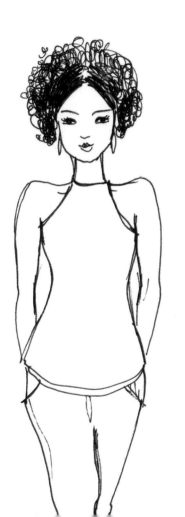

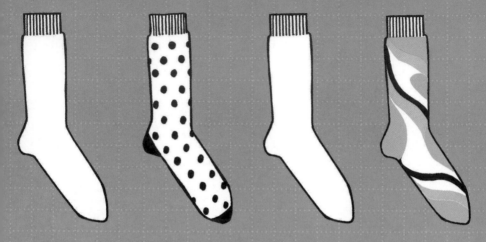

More socks to fill in.

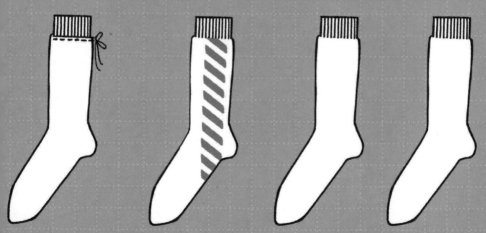

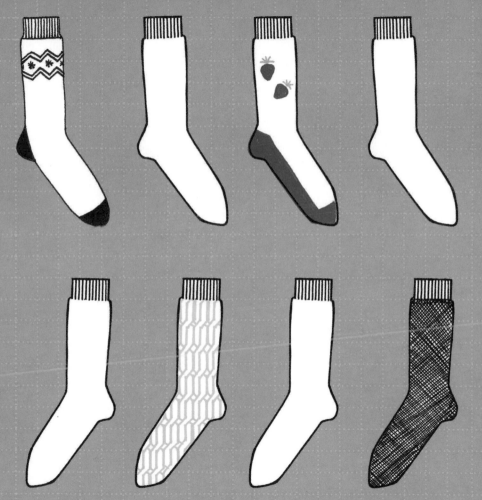

Add details to the doors, roofs and windows on the buildings.

Add some people too.

A fashion designer's bead collection.

125

Fill in the window display in this department store.

126

Draw more hair accessories, make-up and beauty products on this dressing table.

First published in 2015 by Usborne Publishing Ltd., 83-85 Saffron Hill, London, EC1N 8RT, England. www.usborne.com © 2015, 2012 Usborne Publishing Ltd. The name Usborne and the devices ♔ ♕ are Trade Marks of Usborne Publishing Ltd. All rights reserved. No part of this publication may be reproduced, stored in a retrieval system, or transmitted in any form or by any means, electronic, mechanical, photocopy, recording or otherwise, without prior permission of the publisher. UE First published in America 2015.